Usborne

Get ready for school

Alphabet
Sticker Book

You'll find all the stickers at the back of the book.

This book belongs to:

- -

Illustrated by Marina Aizen

Designed by Claire Ever. Words by Jessica Greenwell.

2

Find the stickers to match the letter shapes on the next few pages. Can you colour and trace over the letters too?

stick... **a**   colour... **a**   ...trace. **a**

apple

b   **b**   **b**

bird

I'm Cassie the **cat**. My name begins with 'c'. What else can you spot that begins with 'c'?

c   **c**   **c**

castle

4

g g g

gate

Can you find the sticker to match my letter? I'm Hattie the **horse**.

h h h

house

i i i

Dear Hattie
You are invited to a party

invitation

a b c d e f g h i j k l m

j j j j

jar

k k k k

kite

I'm Leo the lion. What else can you spot on this page that begins with the letter 'l'?

l l l

leaf

n o p q r s t u v w x y z

p p p

pear

q q q

queen

I'm Rosie the **rabbit** and today I'm dressed as a **queen**! Find the stickers for 'q' and 'r'.

r r r

rose

n o p q r s t u v w x y z

Squawk!

S s s s

sun

t t t t

I'm Toby the **tiger** and I'm in my **tent**. Can you trace the letter 't'?

tent

u u u u

umbrella

v v v v

violin

a b c d e f g h i j k l m

windmill

xylophone

I'm Zac the **zebra**. Can you find the 'z' sticker?

yo-yo

zig-zag

n o p q r s t u v w x y z

e f g h

m n o p

Which letter does my name begin with?

My name begins with the last letter of the alphabet.

v w x y z

Trace and match

Trace over each letter and add a picture sticker to match.

a   v   k

What letter does
'yo-yo' begin with?
Can you see it?

d   b

b   y   u

I'm under my
umbrella. Can
you trace over
the letter 'u'?

14

Windy day

Find the stickers to match all the words
and finish this picture.

window

door

vase

gate

bush

envelope

nest

apple

bird

kite

car

win...

puddle

leaf

butterfly

insect

Letters and words

Can you find the sticker for the first letter of each of these words?

a nt

g ate

w atch

f an

e gg

t ent

What letter does **'fan'** begin with? Can you stick it on?

h at

n et

p aint

I'm going to **paint** a **picture**. What letter does **'paint'** begin with?

b all

c ake

s ock

Find the letter

Add a sticker to match the first letter
of each of these words.

bird

fairy

upside down

car

I like playing with
my toys. What letter
do you think 'toys'
begins with?

toys

A

B

C D

elephant

van

robot

ink

nest

leaf

This **doorbell** goes **'ding dong'**. Stick the letter 'd' on the **door**.

Ding dong

door

Animal letters

Find the sticker for the first letter of each animal.

alligator

bear

cat

monkey

rabbit

dog

horse

lion

tiger

zebra

A day at the beach

Find the missing pictures to complete this scene.
Can you match a word sticker to each picture?

ball

boat

net

sand castle

hat

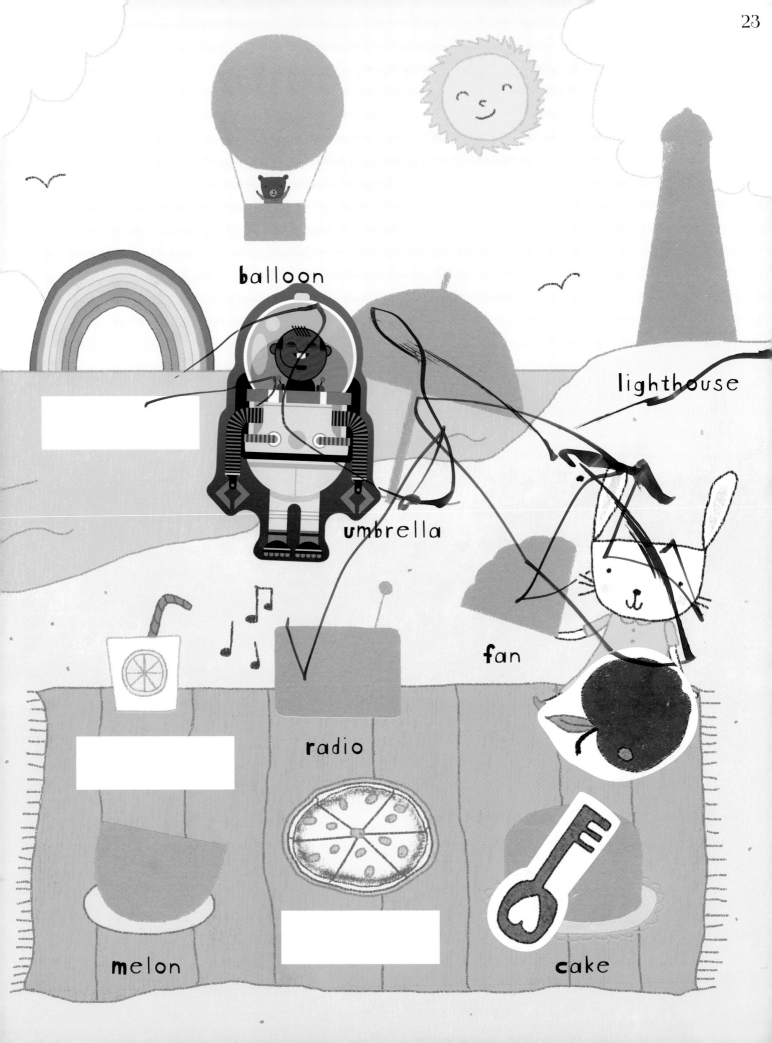

balloon

lighthouse

umbrella

fan

radio

melon

cake

24

Time for bed

Find a picture sticker to match each word in this scene.

rocket

asleep

moon

yawn

lamp

mug

book

teddy

quilt

rug

jack-in-the-box

Letter stickers (pages 2-3)

You can add these stickers to the alphabet line.

Letter stickers (pages 4-5)

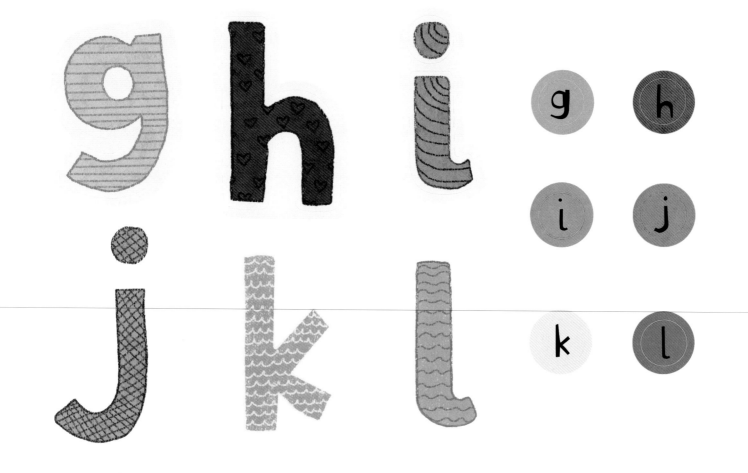

Letter stickers (pages 6-7)

You can add these stickers to the alphabet line.

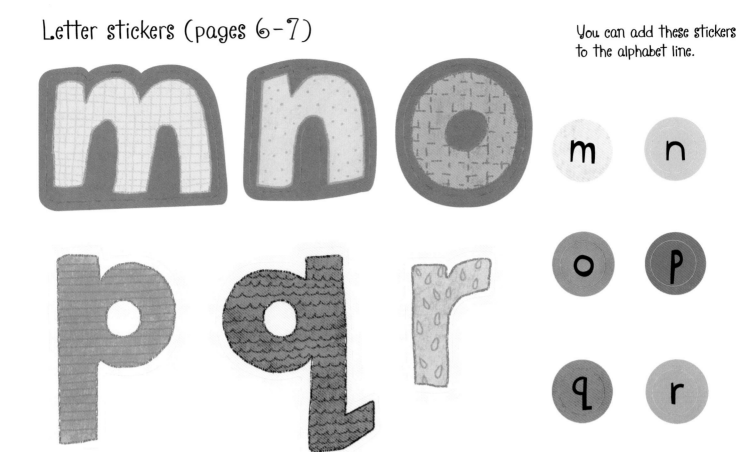

Letter stickers (pages 8-9)

Use these stickers to make the whole alphabet on pages 10–11.

Trace and match (pages 12-13)

windmill

sun

house

necklace

digger

pear

butterfly

octopus

umbrella

carrot

apple

moon

yo-yo

violin

boat

xylophone

key

Windy day (pages 14-15)

s t p e b f

c w n g h a

b c t v n i

f u e r l d

c m t b r

h a l z d

A day at the beach (pages 22-23)

windmill	rainbow	juice	seagull

fish	sun	pizza	water

You can use these extra letter stickers anywhere you like.

a b c d e f g h i j k l m
n o p q r s t u v w x y z
a b c d e f g h i j k l m
n o p q r s t u v w x y z